What happens when the Queen Burps?

Other books in this series:

What Wears a Sock on its Bottom?

How Do You Make a Skeleton Laugh?

What Do You Call a One-eyed Dinosaur?

Poetry Collections by John Foster:

School's Out

Excuses, Excuses

Football Fever

I've Got a Poem For You

Poetry by John Foster:

The Poetry Chest

What happens when the Queen Burps?

Laugh-out-loud jokes, riddles, and rhymes selected by John Foster

Illustrated by Mark Oliver

OXFORD
UNIVERSITY PRESS

OXFORD
UNIVERSITY PRESS

Great Clarendon Street, Oxford OX2 6DP
Oxford University Press is a department of the University of Oxford.
It furthers the University's objective of excellence in research, scholarship, and education by publishing worldwide in

Oxford New York

Auckland Cape Town Dar es Salaam Hong Kong Karachi
Kuala Lumpur Madrid Melbourne Mexico City Nairobi
New Delhi Shanghai Taipei Toronto

With offices in

Argentina Austria Brazil Chile Czech Republic France Greece
Guatemala Hungary Italy Japan Poland Portugal Singapore
South Korea Switzerland Thailand Turkey Ukraine Vietnam

Oxford is a registered trade mark of Oxford University Press
in the UK and in certain other countries

First published 2013

British Library Cataloguing in Publication Data
Data available

ISBN: 978-0-19-275742-5
1 3 5 7 9 10 8 6 4 2

Printed in Great Britain
Paper used in the production of this book is a natural,
recyclable product made from wood grown in sustainable forests.
The manufacturing process conforms to the environmental regulations of the country of origin

CONTENTS

Pardon Me, Your Majesty!	7
What Did You Learn at School Today?	10
Why Did the Teacher Put the Lights On?	12
A Fresh Pair of Legs Up His Sleeve	18
Kiss Me, Baby! I'm Vaccinated	23
Dotty's Potty and Rose's Nose	25
Contemporary Proverbs	27
Dead Funny	29
Give Me the Money or You're Geography	31
Bunnymoons and Quackers	34
Passing Wind	38
Kurt 'n' Rod	41
Hilarious Headlines	44
Why Did Miss Muffet Need a Sat Nav?	46
Pull Yourself Together	49
Ginger Hear the Doorbell?	52
Arctic Architects' Arches Are Artistic Artifices	54
What Wears a Jacket But No Trousers?	58
To Bee or Not To Bee?	60

Who Wrote That? 63

Oil See You Later! 65

Flea Mail and Trapped Flies 67

A Catalogue of Cats 68

While Shepherds Washed Their Socks 70

Brotherly Love 72

Eat Here and Get Gas 74

One Fine Day in the Middle of the Night 76

Elastic Jones and Electric Fred 78

A Jumbo Yeti and a Poultry-geist 80

A Change is as Good as a Rest 82

Deep Fried Worms and Minced Mice 84

Chicks Going Cheap 87

Critics' Choice 89

Why Did the Queen Go to the Dentist? 92

Answers to Puzzles and Riddles 95

PARDON ME, YOUR MAJESTY!

What happens when the queen burps?
She issues a royal pardon.

Which queen hiccuped a lot?
Queen Hic-toria.

Which queen had bad acne?
Mary Queen of Spots.

Who was the first king to have a mobile phone?
William of Orange.

Which King of England was a chiropodist?
William the Corn Curer.

Where was Henry VIII crowned?
On his head.

Why did Henry VIII put skittles on the lawn?
So he could take Anne Boleyn.

At Hallowe'en

At Hallowe'en,
In Bethnal Green
You can see the queen
Bouncing up and down on a trampoline.

The National Anthem (as sung by a barber's shop quartet)

God shave our beardless queen.
Long live our hairless queen.
God shave the queen.
Send her a barber's chair
And while she's sitting there
Shave off her facial hair
God shave the queen.

There were two butcher's shops side by side in the high street. Outside one was a sign saying:
WE MAKE SAUSAGES FOR THE QUEEN.
Outside the shop next door was a sign saying:
GOD SAVE THE QUEEN.

On the Throne

The queen sits alone
On her porcelain throne
Wondering what she should do.
Her business is done
But of paper there's none

And outside they are forming a queue.
What do they call a group of people standing in a queue for a lavatory in Buckingham Palace?
Ladies-in-waiting.

Smelly Socks, Smelly Socks

Smelly socks, smelly socks,
Where have you been?
We've been up to London
To dine with the queen.

The queen gave a sniff,
'What a hideous smell.
Has someone been sick?
Is someone not well?'

Then she sent us all home
With nothing to eat,
Saying, 'Come back next year,
When you've washed your feet.'

WHAT DID YOU LEARN AT SCHOOL TODAY?

What did you learn at school today?
Not enough. I have to go back tomorrow.

Newsflash

$^{7}/_{5}$ OF SCHOOLCHILDREN DO NOT UNDERSTAND FRACTIONS.

A Matter of Interpretation
First pupil: Did you get any A and B grades in your report?
Second pupil: No, I got Es and Fs.
First pupil: What did your dad say?
Second pupil: He said he'd buy me the bike he promised me for getting a good report.
First pupil: But you didn't.
Second pupil: He thinks I did. I told him A meant awful and that E meant excellent and F meant fantastic.

What did the ghostly music teacher play?
Haunting melodies.

Is the maths teacher in a good mood today?
I wouldn't count on it.

I Enjoy Doing My Homework

I enjoy doing my homework,
Even at the weekend.
All my friends tell me that
I must be round the bend.

Old Teachers

What happens to . . .

old English teachers?	They come to a full stop.
old maths teachers?	They are taken away.
old French teachers?	One day they realize that an oeuf is enough.
old art teachers?	They draw their own conclusions.
old drama teachers?	They exit the stage.
old geography teachers?	They go to the ends of the earth.
old history teachers?	They pass their best before date.
old IT teachers?	They log off.

Jim: Why are you scratching your head?
Sam: I've got those arithmetic bugs again.
Jim: Arithmetic bugs—what are they?
Sam: Well, some people call them head lice.
Jim: Then why do you call them arithmetic bugs?
Sam: Because they add to my misery, subtract from my pleasure, divide my attention, and multiply like crazy.

WHY DID THE TEACHER PUT THE LIGHTS ON?

Why did the teacher put the lights on?
Because his pupils were so dim.

Where does ice-cream go to school?
Sundae school.

If a bottle of lemonade were a teacher, what subject would it teach?
Fizzical Education.

Clever Trevor's Classroom Quips

Teacher: You missed school yesterday, didn't you?
Clever Trevor: Yes, but not much.

Teacher: Didn't you hear me call you?
Clever Trevor: Yes, but you told me not to answer back.

Teacher: Didn't you promise to behave?
Clever Trevor: Yes, sir.
Teacher: And didn't I promise to punish you if you didn't?
Clever Trevor: Yes, sir; but since I broke my promise, I don't expect you to keep yours.

Teacher: If Moses were alive today, he'd be considered a remarkable man.
Clever Trevor: He sure would. He'd be thousands of years old!

Teacher : If 'can't' is short for 'cannot', what is 'don't' short for?
Clever Trevor: Doughnut?

Teacher: Spell water.
Clever Trevor: HIJKLMNO.
Teacher: That doesn't spell water.
Clever Trevor: Yes, it does—it's all the letters from H to O.

Teacher: Who wrote *Oliver Twist*?
Clever Trevor: How the Dickens should I know?

Teacher: Can you tell me a proverb?
Clever Trevor: A sock on the foot is worth two on the nose.

Teacher: How much is half of eight?
Clever Trevor: Which way?
Teacher: What do you mean 'which way'?
Clever Trevor: Well, up and down makes three and across makes nought.

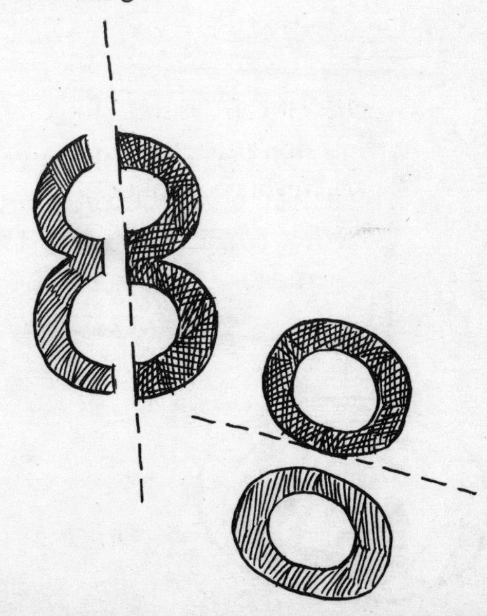

Looking to the Future

End-of-term reports

JACK FROST: Jack remains cool whatever he's doing, but has been absent throughout the summer.

JACK DAW: Bird-brained. Too busy pinching others' ideas, instead of coming up with his own.

JACK O'LANTERN: Erratic attendance, tending to come and go as he pleases, but capable of setting the world on fire.

JACK POT: Gambles on success rather than being prepared to work for it. But has the potential to make someone else millions.

JACK OFALLTRADES: Lacks focus. Consequently, he fails to master any of the skills necessary for any one particular occupation.

JACK RUSSELL: A real terrier, who gets his teeth into everything, but often bites off more than he can chew.

JACK INTHEBOX: Spends most of the time in a world of his own, then springs out suddenly and surprises you with his agility when you least expect it.

A FRESH PAIR OF LEGS UP HIS SLEEVE

Football Commentators' Crazy Comments

He dribbles a lot and the opposition don't like it—
you can see it all over their faces.

If England are going to win this match, they
need to score a goal.

An inch or two either side of the post and that
would have been in.

If history is going to repeat itself, I think we can
expect the same thing again.

The manager still has a fresh pair of legs up his sleeve.

Any time added on is longer if you are winning
and shorter if you are losing.

He's got a knock on his shin there, right above
the knee.

Well, either side could win it, or it could be a draw.

I wouldn't be surprised if this game went all
the way to the finish.

The ball was still moving when it hit the back of the net.

That header was cleared off the line by the crossbar.

Goalkeepers aren't born today until they're in their late twenties or thirties.

That was an inch-perfect pass to no one.

Final Scores

Wanderers 1 Stay-at-homes 0
United 6 Divided 0
Villa 1 Mansion 2
Pompey 1 Caesar 1
Saints 2 Sinners 2
Wednesday 1 Thursday 2
Forest 3 Shrubbery 0
Hammers 0 Screwdrivers 1
Rangers 2 Poachers 1
Gunners 4 Archers 0

The Man in the Wilderness

The Man in the Wilderness asked of me,
'And who will the League Champions be?'
I answered him as I was able,
'The team that finishes top of the table.'

Why is the football pitch so soggy?
Because of all the dribbling.

Sports Quiz

Why was the cricketer given out on the quiz show?
Because he was stumped for an answer.

Why was the basketball player told
to wipe his mouth?
Because he was dribbling on the floor.

Why is a young golfer more
likely to have a car accident?
Because he's an inexperienced driver.

Why are tennis players
often mistaken for lawyers?
*Because they are always
in court.*

Why was the fencing
instructor exasperated?
*Because his pupil kept
missing the point.*

Why did the absent-minded
snooker player give up acting?
Because he kept on forgetting his cue.

Why was the relay runner disqualified
from being a cheerleader?
Because he kept dropping the baton.

Why is a slow racing driver like a bowl of milk?
Because he keeps getting lapped.

Why is a boxer who keeps getting knocked
down like a handful of change?
He's always being counted out.

Why is a football substitute like a magistrate?
Because he is sitting on the bench.

KISS ME, BABY! I'M VACCINATED

Kisses Spread Germs

Kisses spread germs, so it's stated.
Kiss me, baby, I'm vaccinated.

What did the Cyclops say to his girlfriend?
You're the one eye adore.

What did the undertaker say to his girlfriend?
Em-balmy about you.

What did the ram say to his girlfriend?
Will ewe be mine?

What did the python say to his girlfriend?
I've got a crush on you.

What did the magnet say to his girlfriend?
You're very attractive.

What did the witch doctor say to his girlfriend?
Voodoo like to dance?

What did the acrobat say to his girlfriend?
I'm head over heels in love with you.

What did the stag say to his girlfriend?
I love you deerly.

What did the skeleton say to his girlfriend?
I love every bone in your body.

DOTTY'S POTTY AND ROSE'S NOSE

There Was a Young Farmer Called Max

There was a young farmer called Max
Who did not pay any petrol tax.
It was simple you see
For his tractor burned pee
From his grandfather's herd of tame yaks.

There Was a Young Bather from Bewes

There was a young bather from Bewes
Who lay on the banks of the Ouse.
His radio blared
And passers-by stared
For all he had on was the news.

A Young Lady Named Rose

There was a young lady named Rose
Who had a huge wart on her nose.
When she had it removed,
Her appearance improved,
But her glasses slipped down to her toes.

The Old Man from Whitehaven

There was an old man from Whitehaven
Whose whiskers had never been shaven.
He said, 'It is best
For they make a nice nest
In which I can keep my pet raven.'

An Animal-Lover Called Sue

An animal-lover called Sue
Saw a strange beast at the zoo.
When she asked, 'Is it old?'
She was smilingly told,
'It's not an old beast but a gnu!'

A Young Woman Called Dotty

There was a young woman called Dotty
Who said as she sat on her potty,
'It isn't polite
To do this in sight,
But then who am I to be snotty?'

CONTEMPORARY PROVERBS

A person who sneezes without a tissue takes the matter into his own hands.

Two wrongs do not make a right, but two rights make a U-turn.

A person who eats too many prunes gets a good run for their money.

A bird in the hand makes blowing your nose difficult.

A man who keeps his feet on the ground has difficulty putting on his pants.

A person who sees light at the end of a blocked tunnel is an optimist.

A person who burns their bridges before crossing is a pessimist.

Those who eat fast food get indigestion sooner.

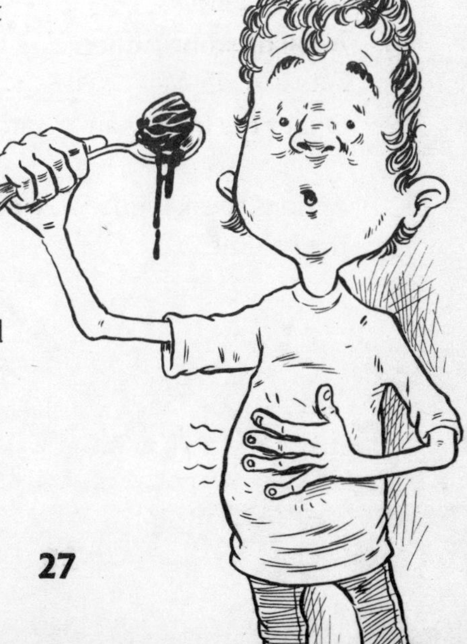

He who looks the most innocent caused
the foul smell.

He who laughs last has difficulty seeing the joke.

Life is like a shower—one wrong turn
and you are in hot water.

New Ends to Old Beginnings

Don't count your chickens . . . eat them.

A bird in the hand . . . is better than a bird
over your head.

Look before you . . . walk into a lamp post.

If at first you don't succeed . . . give up skydiving.

A rolling stone gathers . . . a fair bit of speed.

Out of the frying pan . . . into the stomach.

Actions speak louder . . . when you turn up
the volume.

DEAD FUNNY

A Lovely Finish

Down the road his funeral goes
As sobs and sighs diminish.
He died from drinking varnish—
He had a lovely finish.

First man (on phone): Did you see the announcement of my death in the paper?
Second man: Yes, where are you ringing from?

Aunt Maud

I had written to Aunt Maud
Who was on a trip abroad,
When I heard she died of cramp
Just too late to save the stamp.

Mr Merideth

Here lies one
Now out of breath,
Who lived a merry life
And died a Merideth.

W. W. (William Wilson)

Here lies the body of W. W.
Who never more will trouble you, trouble you.

Johnny Yeast
Here lies Johnny Yeast.
Pardon me for not rising.

Jonathan Blake
Here lies the body
Of Jonathan Blake,
Who pressed the accelerator
Instead of the brake.

Never Say Die
Old bankers never die—they just lose interest.

Old bricklayers never die—they just throw
in the trowel.

Old removal men never die—they just pack it in.

Old drill sergeants never die—they just come
to a halt.

Old electricians never die—they just switch off.

Old chiropodists never die—they just put
their feet up.

Old gardeners never die—they just go to seed.

The Old Man in a Hearse
There was an old man in a hearse
Who murmured, 'This might have been worse;
Of course the expense
Is simply immense,
But it doesn't come out of my purse!'

GIVE ME THE MONEY OR YOU'RE GEOGRAPHY

An armed robber went into a bank and pointed a gun at the cashier and shouted: 'Give me all the money or you're geography!'
'Don't you mean history?' queried the cashier.
'Don't change the subject!' shouted the robber.

Why did the escaped convict saw the legs off his bed?
He wanted to lie low.

POLICE HUNT FOR ESCAPED PRISONERS
The two prisoners who escaped from jail yesterday are still on the run. One is said to be seven feet tall and the other four feet tall. A police spokeswoman said, 'We are looking high and low for them.'

The accused man said to the judge, 'As the Lord is my judge, I am not guilty.'
The judge replied, 'He isn't. I am. You are. Six months.'

Judge to defendant: 'You have been found not guilty of robbery and can leave the court without a stain on your character.'
Defendant: 'Great! Does that mean I can keep the money?'

'Order! Order in court!' said the judge.
'I'll have a cheeseburger and fries, please, your honour,' said the prisoner.

How do you join the police?
You handcuff them together.

What do you call a man who steals cattle?
A beefburglar.

Did you hear about the thief who stole
prunes from the school kitchen?
He's still on the run.

The One That Got Away

At the scene of a bank raid, a police constable came running up to the inspector in charge and said, 'He got away, sir.'
The inspector was furious. 'But I told you to put a man on all the exits,' he shouted. 'How could he have got away?'
'He left by one of the entrances, sir.'

A Safe-Cracking Thief Called MacBride

A safe-cracking thief called MacBride
Once blew a safe-door open wide.
When the dust cleared away
He was filled with dismay
For he found there was nothing inside.

BUNNYMOONS AND QUACKERS

Where do rabbits go when they get married?
On their bunnymoon.

A duck went into a chemist's and asked for some lotion.
'Certainly,' said the chemist. 'Shall I put it on your bill?'

Which farm animal talks too much?
Blah, blah, black sheep.

Why don't owls go out on dates during
a thunderstorm?
Because it's too wet to woo.

What do you call a crate full of ducks?
A box of quackers.

What did the horse say when it reached
the end of its meal?
That's the last straw.

What did the donkey say when it only
had weeds to eat?
Thistle have to do.

What lives in Australia and sticks its
tongue out?
A kanga-rude.

What do canaries do at Hallowe'en?
They go trick or tweeting.

What do you call a pony with a sore throat?
A little hoarse.

What did the mosquito say when it saw
the camel's hump?
Gee, did I do that?

What do you call a fly when it retires?
A flew.

Why are mosquitoes religious?
Because they prey on you.

Why did the owl 'owl?
Because the woodpecker would peck 'er.

What did the porcupine say to the cactus?
Is that you, Mummy?

Why does a tiger have stripes?
So it won't be spotted.

Two parrots were sitting on a perch. One parrot
says to the other, 'Doesn't this perch smell
fishy to you?'

On the Library Shelves

Great Snakes! by Anna Conda.

The Art of Butting by Billy Goat.

TALL STORIES by G. Raffe.

From Trunk to Tail by Ellie Phant.

Snaphappy by Allie Gator.

Balancing Acts by A. C. Lion.

HOPPING MAD by Jack Rabbit.

THERE'S NOWT BETTER THAN A SNOUT by Ann Teater.

An Ass's Tale by Don Key.

Old Hogan's Goat

Old Hogan's goat was feeling fine,
Ate six red shirts from off the line.
Old Hogan grabbed him by the back
And tied him to the railway track.

Now as the train came into sight,
The goat grew pale and green with fright.
He heaved a sigh as if in pain,
Coughed up those shirts and flagged the train.

PASSING WIND

Which Apache chief did the settlers keep well away from?
Passing Wind.

Doctor, doctor, I've got terrible wind.
You're telling me!

Sound Advice

If you are in assembly
And your bottom wants to shout,
Whatever you do,
Don't let it out!

Have You Read?

Bubbles in the Bath by Win D. Bottom.

Keep Well Away by I. Letoneoff.

Who Made that Smell? by Y. R. U. Lookingatme.

OPEN THE WINDOWS by E. Dunanasty.

RUDE NOISES by Ivor Rumblingtum.

Trying Not To Do One by Willie Keepitin.

It Wasn't Me by Scarlett Cheeks.

WHAT A WHIFF by Hugh Dunnit.

Addicted to Baked Beans by F. R. T. Pants.

What do you get if you cross an elephant
with a box of laxatives?
Out of the way.

Did You Hear About . . . ?

Did you hear about my cousin Gus?
He let one off and stank out the bus.

Did you hear about my uncle Jim?
He blew off, then said it wasn't him.

Did you hear why my dad drew a crowd?
His trumpeting was so long and loud.

Did you hear about my prim aunt Nellie?
She passes wind, then says it's not smelly.

Did you hear about my uncle's chum?
When he explodes, it sounds like a drum.

Oh Dear, What Can the Matter Be?

Oh dear, what can the matter be?
Two old ladies got locked in the lavatory.
They were there from Monday to Saturday.
Nobody knew they were there.

I Wandered Lonely As a Cloud

I wandered lonely as a cloud
That floats on high o'er hill and dell
And no one would come near to me
For I'd made a nasty smell.

KURT 'N' ROD

What do you call . . .

a man with a car number plate on his head?
Reg.

a man with scratches on his head?
Claude.

a woman with a radiator on her head?
Anita.

a woman with a box of jewels on her head?
Gemma.

two men who hang over a window?
Kurt 'n' Rod.

a man who stops water flowing out of a reservoir?
Adam.

a girl with a sheep on her head?
Barbara.

a boy with a car on his head?
Jack.

a girl with an oyster on her head?
Pearl.

a boy with a sports hall on his head?
Jim.

a man with a rabbit on his head?
Warren.

a man who is deeply in debt?
Owen.

a girl with a telephone on her head?
Bell.

a man with a cooking pan on his head?
Stu.

a woman with a cat on her head?
Kitty.

a man with a seagull on his head?
Cliff.

Puzzle It Out—A Question of Names
Answer on page 95

Why is Pip like Pop
But Bob not like Rob?
Why is Mum like Dad
But Nan not like Gran?

Why is Anna like Hannah
But Eve not like Steve?
Why is Ada like Otto
But Lil not like Jill?

HILARIOUS HEADLINES

WOMAN HURT WHILE COOKING HER HUSBAND'S BREAKFAST IN A HORRIBLE MANNER.

FALSE CHARGE OF THEFT OF HENS. POLICE ON WILD GOOSE CHASE.

Passengers Hit By Cancelled Trains.

Tips To Avoid Alligators: Don't Swim In Waters Inhabited By Large Alligators.

SHELL FOUND ON BEACH.

THREATENING LETTERS
—MAN ASKS FOR LONG SENTENCE.

STAR'S BROKEN LEG
HITS BOX OFFICE.

SPARE OUR TREES—THEY BREAK WIND.

Man Attacked In Street
By Our Crime Staff.

WHY DID MISS MUFFET NEED A SAT NAV?

Why was the cow so excited that she jumped over the moon?
Because the farmer told her she'd won the lottery.

Why did Miss Muffet need a sat nav?
Because she'd lost her whey.

Why did Tom the piper's son get into
so much trouble?
Because he made a pig of himself.

What happened when the king's men
played a trick on Humpty Dumpty?
He fell for it.

Why didn't Jack Sprat and his wife have
a dishwasher in their house?
Because they licked the platter clean.

How do we know that Jill's friend Jack was
a member of a royal family?
Because when he fell down he broke his crown.

What did the little boy down the lane do
with his bag of wool from the black sheep?
*Spun a yarn about where it came from, then
sold it on e-Bay.*

Why was Mary's little lamb as white as snow?
It had an upset stomach.

What happened to the young mouse that
ran up the clock when it got home?
It got a ticking off.

Little Miss Petal
Little Miss Petal sat on a nettle.
She jumped in the air with a shriek.
Where her knickers were thin
She got such a sting
That she couldn't sit down for a week.

Humpty Dumpty
Humpty Dumpty sat on a wall.
Humpty Dumpty had a great fall.
All the king's horses and all the king's men
Had scrambled eggs for breakfast again.

To Market, To Market
To market, to market,
To buy a DVD.
Home again, home again
To watch it on TV.

Mary, Mary, Quite Contrary
Mary, Mary, quite contrary,
Why are you looking so glum?
'I went for a wee behind the hedge
And a nettle stung my bum!'

Jack the Giantkiller's National Anthem

God save our greatest bean.
May it grow huge and green.
God save our bean.
Let it grow big and flower
Tall as the Eiffel Tower
The tallest there's ever been
God save our bean.

PULL YOURSELF TOGETHER

'Doctor, Doctor,
I feel like a
curtain.'
*'For heaven's
sake, man, pull
yourself together.'*

'Doctor, doctor,
people think I'm a
cricket bat.'
'How's that?'
'Oh, not you as well!'

'Doctor, doctor, I feel like a dog.'
'How long has this been going on?'
'Ever since I was a pup.'

'Doctor, doctor, I think I'm turning into a waste bin.'
'Don't talk rubbish.'

'Doctor, doctor. I can only see black and white.'
'That's because you're a bit off colour.'

'Doctor, doctor, I keep seeing double.'
'Take a seat.'
'Which one?'

What did the lift say to the doctor?
I think I'm coming down with something.

'Doctor, doctor, this lump suddenly appeared on my head.'
'I'm not surprised. It's where a thought hit you.'

'Doctor, doctor, a grasshopper just swore at me.'
'Don't worry, it's just a nasty bug that's going round.'

'Doctor, doctor, my wife thinks she's a lift.'
'Tell her to come in.'
'I can't. She doesn't stop at this floor.'

'Doctor, doctor, I think I've been bitten by a vampire.'
'Drink this glass of water.'
'Will it make me better?'
'No, but I want to see if your neck is leaking.'

'Doctor, doctor, I feel like an ice-cream.'
'So do I. Get me one too.'

Doctoring the Doctor—A Tongue Twister
When a doctor gets sick and another doctor doctors him, does the doctor doing the doctoring have to doctor the doctor the way the doctor being doctored wants to be doctored, or does the doctor doing the doctoring of the doctor doctor the doctor as he wants to do the doctoring?

GINGER HEAR THE DOORBELL?

Knock, knock.
Who's there?
Ginger.
Ginger who?
Ginger hear the doorbell?

Knock, knock.
Who's there?
Dismay.
Dismay who?
Dismay surprise you.

Knock, knock.
Who's there?
Tish.
Tish who?
Bless you!

Knock, knock.
Who's there?
Fitz.
Fitz who?
Fitz not too much trouble,
please open the door.

Knock, knock.
Who's there?
Datsun.
Datsun who?
Datsun awful dress you're wearing.

Knock, knock.
Who's there?
Dan.
Dan who?
Dan just stand there—let me in!

Knock, knock.
Who's there?
Ivor.
Ivor who?
Ivor a sore hand from knocking on this door.

Knock, knock.
Who's there?
Olivia.
Olivia who?
Olivia but I've lost my key.

ARCTIC ARCHITECTS' ARCHES ARE ARTISTIC ARTIFICES

An Alphabet of Tongue Twisters

(To be said out loud as fast as you can.)

Arctic architects' arches are artistic artifices.

The bottom of the butter bucket is the buttered bucket's bottom.

Charlie's chicks cheep, chew cheesy chips
and chomp chocolate.

Drew drew drawings of Deidre drawing
drawings of deer.

Elegant gentleman elephants telephone
elegant lady elephants eloquently.

Five flustered fishes flapping floppy fins.

Grasshoppers gasp as they pass through
the grass, grasping grass.

A hobgoblin on a hobbyhorse hobbles,
hurrying to hobnob with other hobgoblins.

Iris's eyebrows rise in surprise, when Iris
eyes the prizewinning pies.

Jack juggled jamjars gingerly, while Jock
juggled ginger jelly.

Kit's cat Kitty had kittens in Kit's kitchen.

Little Ida Little lied a little, but little Lottie Little
lied a lot.

My Swiss miss misses me and I miss my Swiss miss.

Naughty Norma Norton nicknamed Nichola Nicholas Nicky Knickers.

Olive Oliver ordered original Oriental ornaments for her office.

Pepe prepares pepperoni pizza and plates of pasta in Papa's pizza parlour.

Quiet queen answers quiz questions with quick, quizzical quips.

Rhoda rode down the right road, but Wright rode down the wrong road, until Ida showed Wright the right road.

Shrewd Sue Short's sports shop stocks several sorts of sports shirts and sports shorts.

Two toucans in tutus ate two cans of tinned tuna, then threw the two cans away.

Underwear that's threadbare is not underwear to wear to hide what's under underwear.

Vicious villains visited the village and vandalized valuable vases in the vicarage.

Weightwatchers watch their weight, while overweight diners watch and wait to be waited on by waiters.

Expert egg-examiners explain the excellence of exceptional eggs.

Young yaks yip and yap, yawn and yearn to yackety-yak.

Zany Zoe zealously zaps zillions of zooming zigger-zaggers.

WHAT WEARS A JACKET BUT NO TROUSERS?

Riddle It Out—**Answers on page 95**

1. At the bottom I've a point.
   At the top I've a head.
   Hit me or tap me and what I'm able to do
   Is to hold wooden things together for you.

2. I can quickly heat what you eat.
   But carefully follow each instruction.
   Metal inside me can cause my destruction.

3. I leave my mark on page or card.
   But you can break me, if you press me too hard.

4. What has a spine but no bones, leaves but
   no branches?

5. What wears a jacket but no trousers.
Has no bones but a skin?
Is brown on the outside
But white within?

6. What I am called by name
And what I'm made of are the same.
Don't drop me whatever you do
And I will give lip-service to you.

7. A man rides into town on Friday, stops for three nights and leaves on Saturday.
How is this possible?

8. You don't want to have one but, if you have one, you don't want to lose it.
What am I?

9. I am a home when I'm at home, and I'm still a home when I'm in a park.
The further you pull me away from home, the further I'll be your home from home.

10. I am there in open but not in closed.
I am also in spend but not in save.
I am there in suspense and in happening.
In your hand I can make my mark.

Punctuation Puzzle

Can you punctuate this verse so that it makes sense?

Every lady in the land
Has twenty nails on each hand
Five and twenty on hands and feet
This is true without deceit

Answer on page 95

TO BEE OR NOT TO BEE?

What do bees say as a warning to other bees to take care?
Bee-ware.

What is a bee's favourite quotation?
To bee or not to bee? That is the question.

What do you call an interfering bee?
A buzzybody.

What do you call an angry bee that is always complaining?
A grumblebee.

What did the bee
say to the wasp that was
annoying him?
Buzz off!

Where do bees buy bargains?
Bumble sales.

Which TV channel do bees watch most?
Bee Bee Cee One.

What is a bee's favourite vegetable?
Bee-troot.

What does an unhygienic bee suffer from?
Bee-O.

Why did the bee fly with its legs crossed?
Because it was desperate to get to the Bee Pee station.

How do bees stop themselves from smelling?
They use bee-odorants.

What is a young girl bee's favourite toy?
Bar-bee.

Where do bees go on their holidays?
Stingapore.

What do bees use to keep their hair tidy?
A honeycomb.

How do bees communicate with distant relatives?
They give them a buzz.

What is a bee's favourite cartoon character?
Buzz Lightyear.

What bee is good for your health?
Vitamin Bee.

What does a bee parent say to a naughty young bee?
Beehive yourself.

What do bees wear to the beach?
Bee-kinis.

What do bees say when they get back from work?
Honey, I'm home.

WHO WROTE THAT?

Batty Booklists

Time for School by R. U. Upjohn.

Adding for Beginners by Juan and Juan Mextoo.

Indian Pasties by Sam Osas.

How to Resign by Ike Witt.

To Your Advantage by Ben E. Fit.

Church Services by Eve N. Song.

A JAPANESE WARRIOR'S TALE by Sam Urai.

A Life in Films by Holly Wood.

I'M WARNING YOU by B. Ware.

A Reptile's Story by Liz Ard.

More Batty Books

Foretelling the Future by Clair Voyant.

Maths Made Easy by Cal Q. Lator.

Who Told You? by A. Dickie Bird.

Hide and Seek by P. Kaboo.

UNDER FALSE PRETENCES by Fay King.

Upstairs and Downstairs by S. Calator.

Diary of a Fraudster by M. Bezzler.

All Creatures Very Small by Minnie Beasts.

SECURING YOUR TENT by Guy Ropes.

It's a Sticky Business by S. L. O. Tape.

A LAUGH A MINUTE by T. Hee-Hee.

OIL SEE YOU LATER!

Why are top golfers like careful motorists?
Both are good drivers.

Why do hairdressers get to their destination quicker than other drivers?
They know all the short cuts.

Why did the car get a puncture?
Because it didn't see the fork in the road.

What did the jack say to the car?
Can I give you a lift?

What kind of snakes do you find on cars?
Windscreen vipers.

Where do you go to buy second-hand footwear?
Car boot sales.

NEWSFLASH
Motorists were stuck in a five-mile traffic jam when a glue tanker overturned in Berkshire.

What did the car say as it left the petrol station?
Oil see you later!

When is a car not a car?
When it turns into a road.

Which Car?
Which car do they drive?
A photographer—a Ford Focus.
A zookeeper—a Fiat Panda.
A sweet shop owner—a Volkswagen Polo.
An RAF pilot—a Triumph Spitfire.
An astronaut—a Toyota Space Cruiser.
A ghost—a Rolls Royce Phantom.
A birdwatcher—a Robin Reliant.
An insect expert—a Volkswagen Beetle.
A marine biologist—a Corvette Stingray.

FLEA MAIL AND TRAPPED FLIES

What does a computer do when it is hungry?
It goes out for a byte.

Why did you kick the computer?
Because you told me to boot it up.

What goes 'Choo, choo, choo' when searching the net?
Thomas the Search Engine.

What happens if you get a megabyte?
It megahertz.

Why are flies afraid to use computers?
They may get tangled in the web.

How do fleas communicate with each other?
By flea-mail.

A CATALOGUE OF CATS

Why are cats good at playing the piano?
Because they are very mews-ical.

What do cats put in their lemonade?
Mice cubes.

What do Chinese cats eat?
Egg fried mice.

What do you call a cat that's just eaten a duck?
A duck-filled fatty puss.

How do cats keep up-to-date with current affairs?
They read the mewspapers.

Why do cats do well in exams?
They give purrfect answers.

What did one cat say to the other cat when
it was speechless?
What's the matter? Has a human got your tongue?

Kittystein

WHILE SHEPHERDS WASHED THEIR SOCKS

While Shepherds Washed Their Socks by Night

While shepherds washed their socks by night,
All seated round the tub,
A bar of scented soap came down
And they began to scrub.

Good King Wenceslas
Good King Wenceslas looked out
On the Feast of Stephen.
A snowball hit him on the snout
And made it all uneven.
Brightly shone his conk that night,
Though the pain was cruel,
Till the doctor came in sight,
Riding on a mu-oo-el.

We Four Beatles of Liverpool Are
We four Beatles of Liverpool are,
Paul in a taxi, John in a car.
George on a scooter, blowing his hooter,
Following Ringo Starr.

What do you shout when Father Christmas
takes the register at school?
Present!

What is Father Christmas suffering from if
he's afraid of coming down chimneys?
Santaclaustrophobia.

Extract from a Reindeer's Diary
Boxing Day
Slept.

How does Good King Wenceslas like his pizza?
Deep and crisp and even.

Knock, knock.
Who's there?
Wenceslas.
Wenceslas who?
Wenceslas bus home?

BROTHERLY LOVE

Mind the Paintwork

Willie, with a thirst for gore,
Nailed his sister to the door.
Mother said, with humour quaint:
'Now, Willie dear, don't scratch the paint.'

Sister Nell

In the family drinking well
Willie pushed his sister Nell—
She's there yet, because it kilt her,
Now we'll have to buy a filter.

Not Wanted

Willie had a baby sister,
But he wanted a baby brother.
So left alone with her one night
Up the chimney he did shove her.

Willie and His Sister Sue

Willie pushed his sister Sue
Into a tub he'd filled with glue,
Laughed and pushed in her friend Heather,
Saying, 'Friends should stick together.'

A Spider in the Bath

Little Willie for a laugh
Put a spider in the bath.
He put one in the basin too
And another in the loo.
When his sister screamed and swore,
He put one underneath the door.
His mother who was passing by,
Hearing her daughter give a cry,
Said, 'Willie, you're old
enough to know
You should not
treat those
spiders so.'

EAT HERE AND GET GAS

Nutty Notices

ELEPHANTS PLEASE STAY IN YOUR CARS—*in a wildlife reserve.*

EAT HERE AND GET GAS—*outside an American service station.*

COME IN YOUR THOUSANDS. THE HALL HOLDS FIVE HUNDRED. —*leaflet advertising a concert.*

SATURDAY NIGHT DANCE VERY EXCLUSIVE. EVERYBODY WELCOME.—*on the door of a dance hall.*

Customers Giving Orders Will Be Promptly Executed—*outside a tailor's workshop.*

OUR MOTTO IS TO GIVE OUR CUSTOMERS THE LOWEST PRICES AND WORKMANSHIP—*in a dry cleaner's window.*

THIS IS A GENUINE OFFER—NO CONNECTION WITH ANY OTHER FIRM WHO ARE SELLING RUBBISH—*from an advertising circular.*

DON'T STAND THERE AND BE HUNGRY.
COME IN AND GET FED UP.—*in a restaurant window.*

Let Us Meat Your Needs—*outside a butcher's shop.*

BRING YOUR MENDING HERE
AND WE'LL STITCH YOU UP—*in a tailor's window.*

WE CAN FIX ANYTHING (Please knock on the door—the bell doesn't work)—*on the door of a repair shop.*

Best Scotch beef from Wales—*sign in butcher's window.*

CLOSED DUE TO STAFF SICKNESS—*sign on door of health food shop.*

BACK SOON. GONE TO TEE.—*sign outside golf shop.*

PULL. If that doesn't work, PUSH.
If that doesn't work, we're closed.—*on the door of a post office.*

ONE FINE DAY IN THE MIDDLE OF THE NIGHT

One Fine Day in the Middle of the Night
One fine day in the middle of the night
Two dead men got up to fight.
Back to back they faced each other,
Drew their swords and shot each other.

Time's Up

It was full-time at the fairy tale football match,
With twenty minutes to go.
The detective had questioned the Knave of Hearts
And the beanstalk had started to grow.
Humpty Dumpty was singing carols.
Cinderella had found her shoe.
A goose was laying the table
And the mice were forming a queue.
The king had pardoned the sparrow.
The maids were all dancing a jig
When the judge tripped over a toadstool
And Tom ran away with his wig!

The Lord Said Unto Moses

The Lord said unto Moses, 'Come forth!'
But he slipped on a banana skin and came fifth.

Jolly Roger

Jolly Roger lived up a tree.
You climbed up by a rope.
I'd often go for a cup of tea
Which he brewed up with some soap.

Once I found a sock in mine,
It made me wince a bit,
But Roger told me, 'Never mind.
It's old and doesn't fit.'

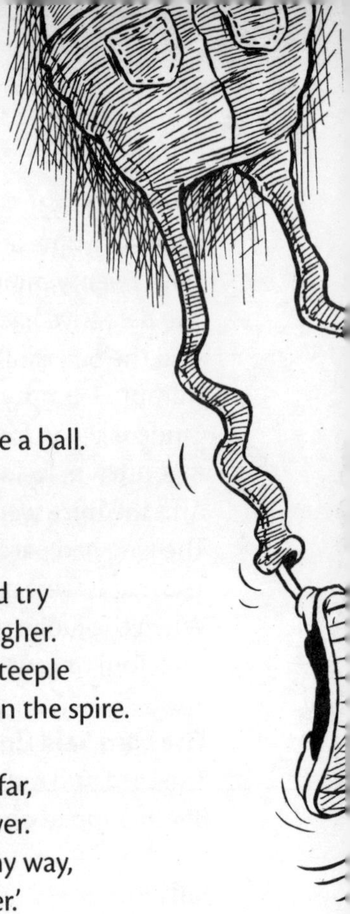

ELASTIC JONES AND ELECTRIC FRED

Elastic Jones

Elastic Jones had rubber bones.
He could bounce up and down like a ball.
When he was six, one of his tricks
Was jumping a ten-foot wall.

As the years went by, Elastic would try
To jump higher, and higher, and higher.
He amazed people by jumping a steeple
Though he scratched his behind on the spire.

But, like many a star, he went too far,
Getting carried away with his power.
He boasted one day, 'Get out of my way,
I'm going to jump Blackpool Tower.'

He took off from near the end of the pier,
But he slipped and crashed into the top.
Amid cries and groans, Elastic Jones
Fell into the sea with a plop.

Electric Fred

Electric Fred has wires in his head
And one hundred watt light bulbs for eyes,
Which means, of course, he can talk in morse
Or flash red, white, and blue with surprise.

Just for a lark, he can shoot a spark
For three hundred feet out of his nose.
Wear rubber bands, if you shake his hands,
Or the current will tingle your toes.

Sometimes he chews a fifteen amp fuse
Or recharges himself via the fire.
Just give him jolts of thousands of volts
And you'll find he's a really live wire!

A JUMBO YETI AND A POULTRY-GEIST

What do you get if you cross Bigfoot with an elephant?
A jumbo yeti.

What do you get if you cross a rabbit with a kettle?
A hot cross bunny.

What do you get if you cross a ghost with a chicken?
A poultry-geist.

What do you get if you cross a pig with
a naked person?
Streaky bacon.

What do you get if you cross a large
computer with a beefburger?
A big mac.

What do you get when you cross a computer
with one million mosquitoes?
A gigabite.

What do you get if you cross a fast food outlet
with a childhood illness?
Kentucky Fried chickenpox.

What do you get if you cross a chicken with
a cement mixer?
A brick-layer.

What do you get if you cross a skunk with
a boomerang?
A bad smell that you can't get rid of.

What do you get if you cross a snake
with a magician?
An abra da cobra.

What do you get if you cross baked beans
with onions?
Tear gas.

What do you get if you cross a pelican with a zebra?
Across the road safely.

What do you get if you cross a lake with
a leaking boat?
About halfway.

What do you get if you cross a cow
with a crystal ball?
A message from the udder side.

A CHANGE IS AS GOOD AS A REST

Mottoes
What is a chameleon's motto?
A change is as good as a rest.

What is a snail's motto?
Better late than never.

What is a frog's motto?
Look before you leap.

What is the screwdriver's motto?
One good turn deserves another.

What is the roundabout's motto?
What goes around comes around.

What is a weathercock's motto?
Go with the blow.

What is the magician's motto?
Never miss a trick.

DEEP FRIED WORMS AND MINCED MICE

The Witch's Favourite Foods

Bottled bluebottles
Lizard's eyes
Deep fried worms
Flies in pies.

Rat's tail soup
Cockroach crunchies
Beetle butties
Maggot munchies.

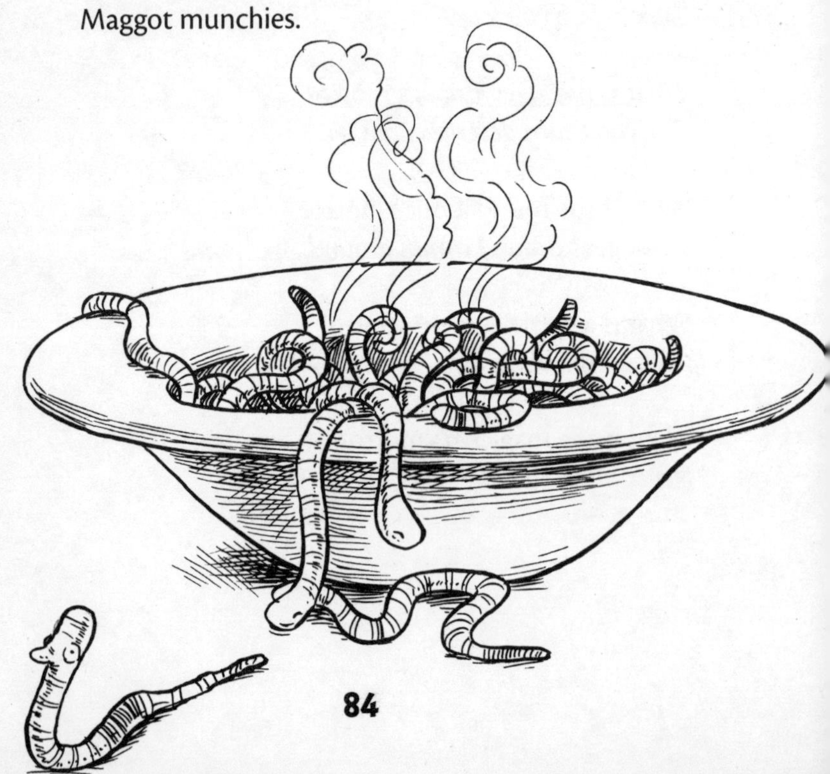

Wasps on toast
Spiced lice
Spider cakes
Minced mice.

Snakeskin tart
Boiled rook's wings
These are a few
Of my favourite things.

Witches' Wheezes

Why couldn't the witch's victim move?
Because he was spellbound.

What do you call a wizard from outer space?
A flying sorcerer.

How many witches does it take to change a lightbulb?
It depends what you want it to change into.

Why do witches get stiff joints?
They get broomatism.

The Graveyard Theatre Presents–
GHOULDILOCKS
AND THE THREE SCARES

A HALLOWE'EN PHANTOMIME
FOR ALL THE FAMILY
Starring
Bella Donna as Ghouldilocks
Ed Underisarm as the Headless Horseman
Count Dracula as the Villainous Redneck
Frank Enstein as Mister Macabre

Tickets on sale nightly from midnight to tombtime.
Special rates for mummies and their fiends.

'Rib-tickling entertainment' *Skeleton Times*
'Wicked!' *Witches Weekly*
'You'll laugh your head off' *Ghost Gazette*
'Dead funny' *Undertakers News*

CHICKS GOING CHEAP

Absurd Adverts

FOR SALE: ONE-DAY-OLD CHICKS GOING CHEAP

CRASH COURSES ARE AVAILABLE
FOR THOSE WISHING TO DRIVE QUICKLY.

Decorator. Specializes in inferior work.
Immediate attention.

FOR SALE: Large crystal vase by lady slightly cracked.

For sale: Ford Granada hearse with new body.

WHY BREAK YOUR CHINA WASHING UP?
DO IT AUTOMATICALLY IN A DISHWASHER.

Are you illiterate? Write for information.

FOR SALE
Violin—really cheap. No strings attached.

DOG FOR SALE. EATS ANYTHING; ESPECIALLY FOND OF CHILDREN.

Antique desk suitable for lady with thick legs and large drawers.

Nice parachute. Never opened—used once.

Once you have dealt with us you will recommend others.

Second-hand tombstone for sale. Extraordinary bargain for family named Schwarzendorfer.

DENTAL SERVICES 4 YOU—
TEETH EXTRACTED WITH THE GREATEST PAINS.

CRITICS' CHOICE

Ten Books For You To Read

Covered in Fleas	It'll make your skin crawl.
An Insomniac's Diary	It'll keep you awake at night.
How to Build a Robot	It's riveting.

The History of Glue	I couldn't put it down.
The Howling Werewolf	It's spine-chilling.
The Witch's Curse	It's spellbinding.
A FISHERMAN'S CATCH	It'll have you hooked.
Juggling Plates	It's smashing.
How to Use Sellotape	It's gripping.
The Mythical Monster	It's unbelievable.

And Ten Books Not to Read

How to Drill Holes	It's boring.
The Dimwit	It's dull.
The Never-Ending Story	It goes on and on and on and on and on . . .
Tedious Times	It's not interesting.
Life in the Cot	It's babyish.
In Hot Water	It's not cool.
Gobbledegook	It's senseless.
Going Round and Round in Circles	It'll make you dizzy.
Foul Smells	It'll make your stomach churn.
Mouldy Food	It's a sickening story.

WHY DID THE QUEEN GO TO THE DENTIST?

What's the best time to go to the dentist?
Tooth-hurty.

What do you use to fix a broken tooth?
Toothpaste.

Why did the queen go to the dentist?
To get her teeth crowned.

Why are dentists unhappy?
Because they are always looking down in the mouth.

What did the judge ask the dentist to do?
He asked her to extract the tooth, the whole tooth, and nothing but the tooth.

What do you call an old dentist?
Long in the tooth.

What does the dentist of the year receive as his prize?
A little plaque.

Why did the artist decide to become a dentist?
Because he was good at drawing teeth.

How do polar explorers stop their mouths
from freezing up?
They grit their teeth.

ANSWERS TO PUZZLES AND RIDDLES

Puzzle it Out—A Question of Names

Some of the names e.g. Pip, Mum, Dad are words which are the same when read backwards or forwards. A word which reads the same when read backwards or forwards is called a palindrome.

Riddle It Out

1. a nail; 2. a microwave; 3. a pencil; 4. a book; 5. a potato; 6. a glass; 7. His horse was called Friday; 8. an argument; 9. a caravan; 10. a pen.

Punctuation Puzzle

Every lady in the land
Has twenty nails. On each hand
Five, and twenty on hands and feet.
This is true without deceit.

ACKNOWLEDGEMENTS

This collection © Copyright John Foster 2013
The following poems are © Copyright John Foster 2013
and may not be reproduced without permission:

'An Alphabet of Tongue Twisters'
'At Hallowe'en'
'A Question of Names'
'A Spider in the Bath'
'Elastic Jones'
'Electric Fred'
'Final Scores'
'Ghouldilocks and the Three Scares'
'Jack the Giantkiller's National Anthem'
'Mary, Mary, Quite Contrary'
'Mottoes'
'On the Throne'
'The Man in the Wilderness'
'The Witch's Favourite Foods'
'Time's Up'
'Willie and His Sister Sue'
'Little Miss Petal'
'Looking to the Future'
'Smelly Socks, Smelly Socks'